DUNGEON OF SEVEN DOOMS

by
Michael Dahl

illustrated by
Roberta Pares

Raintree

www.raintreepublishers.co.uk
Visit our website to find out
more information about
Raintree books.

To order:
☎ Phone 0845 6044371
🖶 Fax +44 (0) 1865 312263
✉ Email myorders@raintreepublishers.co.uk

Customers from outside the UK please telephone +44 1865 312262

Raintree is an imprint of Capstone Global Library Limited,
a company incorporated in England and Wales having its registered office at
7 Pilgrim Street, London, EC4V 6LB
– Registered company number: 6695582

Story by Michael Dahl
Illustrated by Roberta Pares
Colour by Glass House Graphics
Series Designer: Brann Garvey
Series Editor: Donald Lemke
Editorial Director: Michael Dahl
Art Director: Bob Lentz
Creative Director: Heather Kindseth
Originated by Capstone Global Library Ltd
Printed and bound in China by Leo Paper Products Ltd

ISBN 978 1 406 24323 9 (paperback)
16 15 14 13 12
10 9 8 7 6 5 4 3 2 1

British Library Cataloguing in Publication Data
A full catalogue record for this book is available
from the British Library.

"WHAT DUNGEON IS SO DARK AS ONE'S OWN HEART?"

– NATHANIEL HAWTHORNE

PRINCE KALBAN

IN AN ANCIENT KINGDOM OF LIGHT AND SHADOW, ON THE NIGHT OF THE DRAGON'S STAR, PRINCE KALBAN IMPRISONS HIS TWIN BROTHER, THE RIGHTFUL HEIR TO THE THRONE. THEN KALBAN AND HIS HENCHMEN BEGIN THEIR MARCH THROUGH THE HEAVILY GUARDED PALACE, TO ATTACK THE KING, AND CROWN THE EVIL KALBAN AS THE NEXT RULER . . .

GOOD VS EVIL

PRINCE AREL

ON THE NIGHT OF THE DRAGON'S STAR, AREL IS IMPRISONED BY HIS EVIL TWIN BROTHER IN THE DUNGEON OF SEVEN DOOMS. NO ONE HAS EVER ESCAPED FROM THE WEIRD PRISON. BUT AREL MUST FIND A WAY THROUGH THE MAZE OF DEATH AND SHADOW, TO DEFEAT HIS BROTHER, AND RESCUE THE KINGDOM'S RIGHTFUL RULER . . .

THERE ARE ARCHERS IN THE WALL!

KLINK!

AHHH!

AHHH!

WHAM!

SSSSSS

BOOM!

CLICK

SPLOOSH!

MY FATHER.

28

MY BROTHER.

THE DUNGEON OF ILLUSIONS!

SCRIPT BY

Michael Dahl is the author of more than 200 books for children and young adults. He has won the AEP Distinguished Achievement Award three times for his non-fiction. His Finnegan Zwake mystery series was shortlisted twice by the Anthony and Agatha awards. He has also written the Library of Doom series and the Dragonblood books. He is a featured speaker at conferences on graphic novels and high-interest books for boys.

VISUAL GLOSSARY

SWORD FIGHTS

In a graphic novel, even noise can be shown visually. During the sword fights, bursts of light show us that the swords have connected and that the blades are making a bright, metallic sound.

THE HYDRA

Authors and illustrators often include characters or ideas from other people's stories in their own work. The seven-headed dragon, or Hydra, comes from the ancient Greek myth of Hercules.

BROKEN MIRROR

A single object can symbolize more than one meaning. The broken mirror at the end of the story can show the outcome of a battle, or tell us that an image, or illusion, has been destroyed.

THE FALLING TAPESTRY

Graphic novels use parallel, or side-by-side, action to compare things we normally would not consider. Could being buried under a gigantic carpet feel like being crushed by a monster?

ACTION LINES

Action lines in graphic novels indicate speed, force, or intense emotion - or all three at once. We know that Prince Arel has hit the locked door with great force because of the lines that flow out from him, and because of the burst between his shoulder and the door itself.

VISUAL QUESTIONS

1. This adventure is entitled *Dungeon of Seven Dooms*. Each doom is introduced visually throughout Prince Arel's journey. Can you locate all seven dangers?

2. Although the twin princes face parallel dangers, they take different paths. Kalban avoids arrows from above using a shield. Arel overcomes blades from below by destroying his own sword. What do their different actions tell us about the brothers?

3. When Arel enters the metal chamber filled with water, he steps on a button and activates a hidden mechanism. Visual clues in the following panels tell you something is happening to the water. What?

4. The evil prince is about to strike down the king, but he stops. The panel shows him turning around. Why? And can you tell from the illustrations what he is feeling?

5. Arel's sword seems to pass harmlessly through Kalban. Why? Do the following panels hint at where Arel is? Do they explain why Kalban was not harmed?

6. As the evil Kalban is dragged down into the dungeons, the illustrator has represented all seven dooms in the artwork. Can you identify them all?

CREATING THE BOOK

THE MANUSCRIPT

Graphic novels are often created by two different people – a writer and an illustrator. Even when a book contains few words, the writer must provide detailed notes called "scene descriptions", instructing the content of each panel.

A page from the *Dungeon of Seven Dooms* manuscript:

Page 12

UPPER
Panel 1
KALBAN looks down and sees some palace guards looking up at him and his men from the terrace below. The guards are pointing and obviously angered at the evil prince's attack on the king's private quarters.

Panel 2
KALBAN and his henchmen reach the top of the wall. They are swinging over the edge of the terrace they were climbing towards.

Panel 3
KALBAN takes a nearby torch and lights the vines.

LOWER
Panel 1
AREL swings his torch at the bats.

Panel 2
Another angle of AREL fighting off the bats. He is trying to inch his way through the chamber of vines and bats.

Panel 3
AREL's torch lights the vines. Many of them begin to burn and smoke.

PENCILS

After receiving the manuscript from the writer, the illustrator creates rough sketches called "pencils". The writer and editor of the book review these drawings, making sure all corrections are made before continuing to the next stage.

From page 12 of *Dungeon of Seven Dooms*:

INKS

When illustrations have been approved by the editor, an artist, sometimes called an "inker", draws over the pencils in ink. This stage allows readers to see the illustration more easily in print.

COLOURS

Next, the inks are sent to a "colourist" who adds colour to each panel of art.

When the art is completed, designers add the final touches, including speech bubbles and sound effects. Turn to page 12 to see the final version.

EVERY STORY
HAS TWO SIDES...

GOOD vs EVIL

Adventure

Fantasy

Science Fiction

Horror

COLLECT THEM ALL!

STOP

CH GOOD VS EVIL BOOK HAS TWO STO
E BLUE AND ONE RED – BUT YOU CAN
IT IN MANY DIFFERENT WAYS . . .

THE BLUE
E END. THEN
D READ THE
STORY.

OR S
RED
THE